Eureka Math™

A Story of Units

Common Core, Inc. (commoncore.org) is a non-profit organization formed in 2007 to advocate for a content-rich liberal arts education in America's K-12 schools. To improve education in America, we create curriculum materials, conduct professional development, and also promote programs, policies, and initiatives at the local, state, and federal levels that provide students with challenging, rigorous instruction in the full range of liberal arts and sciences.

Common Core, Inc. is not affiliated with the Common Core State Standards Initiative.

Special thanks go to the Gordan A. Cain Center and to the Department of Mathematics at Louisiana State University for their support in the development of *Eureka Math*.

Published by Common Core

Common Core
1016 16th Street NW, 7th Floor
Washington, DC 20036
Phone 202.223.1854
Web commoncore.org
Email info@commoncore.org

Printed in the U.S.A.
This book may be purchased from the publisher at commoncore.org
10 9 8 7 6 5 4 3 2 1

ISBN 978-1-63255-033-0

Name ______________________________ Date ______________

1. Use the place value chart and arrows to show how the value of the each digit changes. The first one has been done for you.

   a. 3.452 × 10 = 34.52

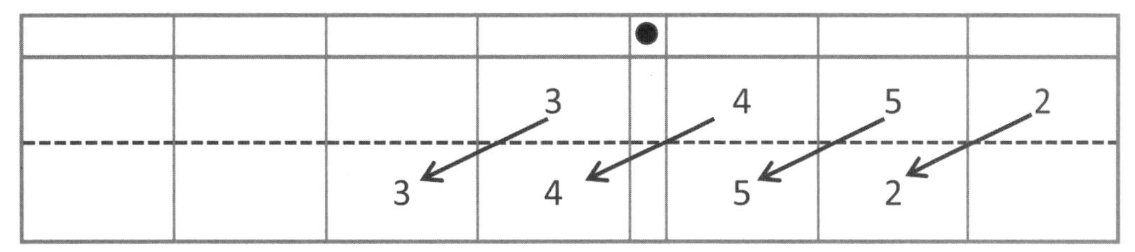

   b. 3.452 × 100 = ________

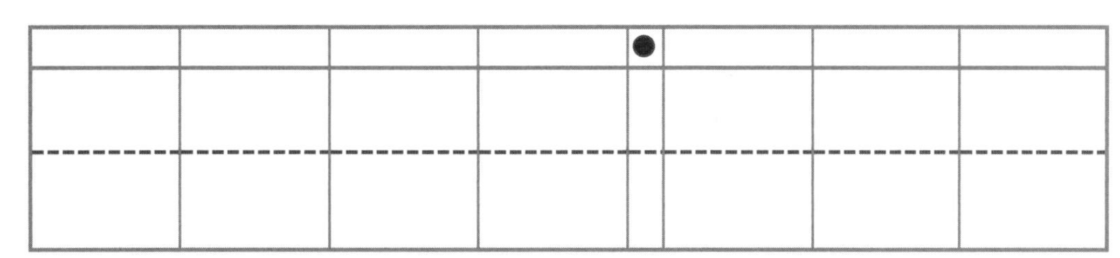

   c. 3.452 × 1,000 = ________

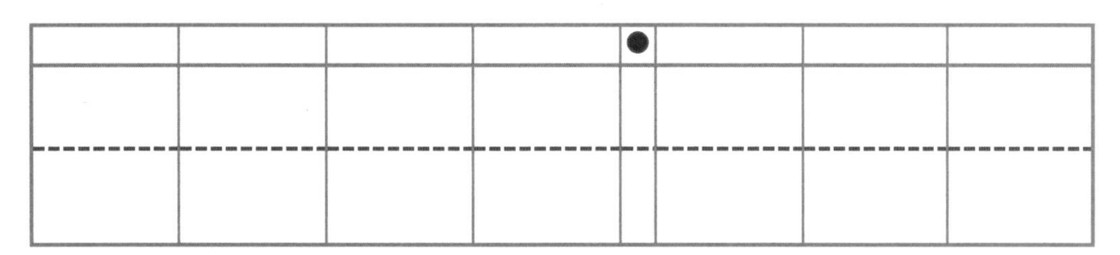

   d. Explain how and why the value of the 5 changed in (a), (b), and (c).

2. Use the place value chart and arrows to show how the value of each digit changes. The first one has been done for you.

   a. 345 ÷ 10 = 34.5

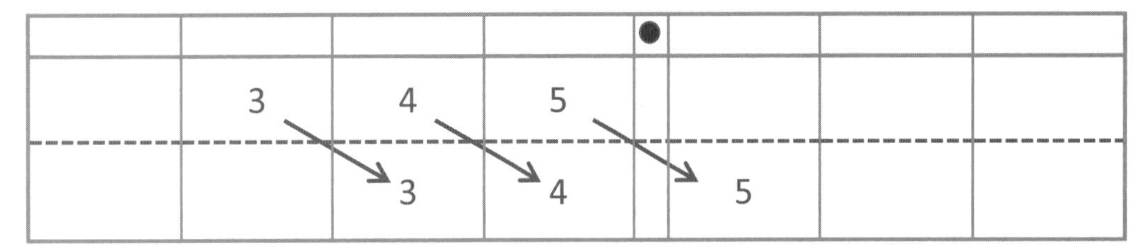

   b. 345 ÷ 100 = ___________

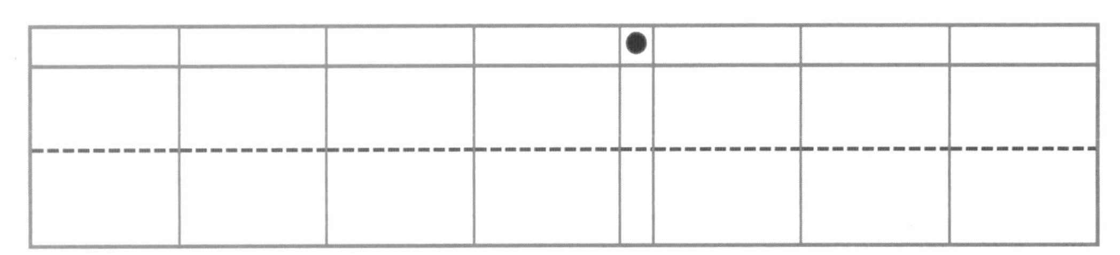

   c. 345 ÷ 1,000 = ___________

				•			

   d. Explain how and why the value of the 4 changed in the quotients in (a), (b), and (c).

3. A manufacturer made 7,234 boxes of coffee stirrers. Each box contains 1,000 stirrers. How many stirrers did they make? Explain your thinking, and include a statement of the solution.

4. A student used his place value chart to show a number. After the teacher instructed him to multiply his number by 10, the chart showed 3,200.4. Draw a picture of what the place value chart looked like at first.

				•			

a. Explain how you decided what to draw on your place value chart. Be sure to include your reasoning about how the value of each digit was affected by the multiplication. Use words, pictures, or numbers.

5. A microscope has a setting that magnifies an object so that it appears 100 times as large when viewed through the eyepiece. If a tiny insect is 0.095 cm long, how long will the insect appear in centimeters through the microscope? Explain how you know.

Name ______________________________ Date ________________

1. Use the place value chart and arrows to show how the value of each digit changes. The first one has been done for you.

   a. 4.582 × 10 = 45.82

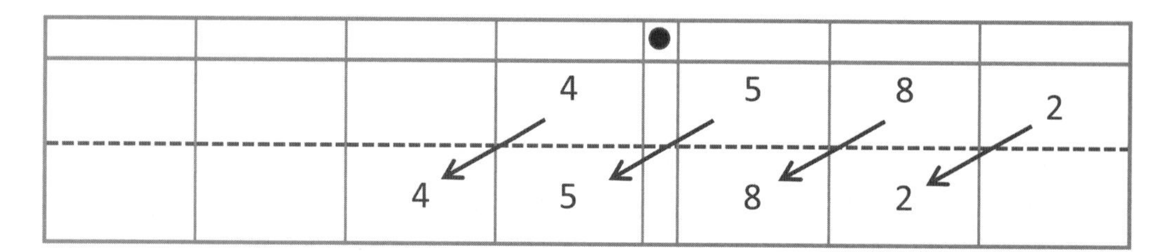

   b. 7.281 × 100 = ____________

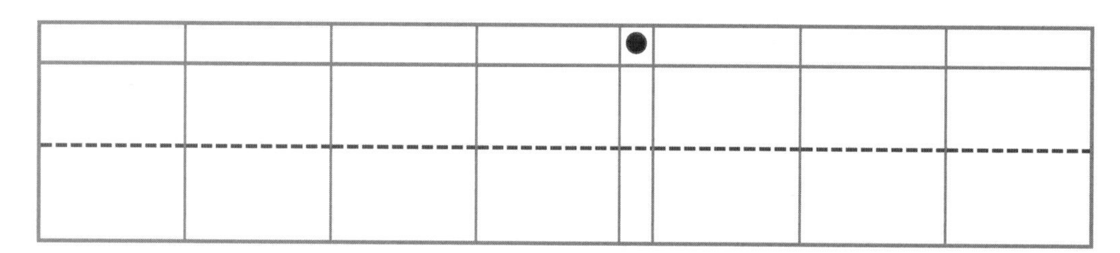

   c. 9.254 × 1,000 = ____________

   d. Explain how and why the value of the 2 changed in (a), (b), and (c).

2. Use the place value chart and arrows to show how the value of each digit changes. The first one has been done for you.

   a. $2.46 \div 10 =$ 0.246

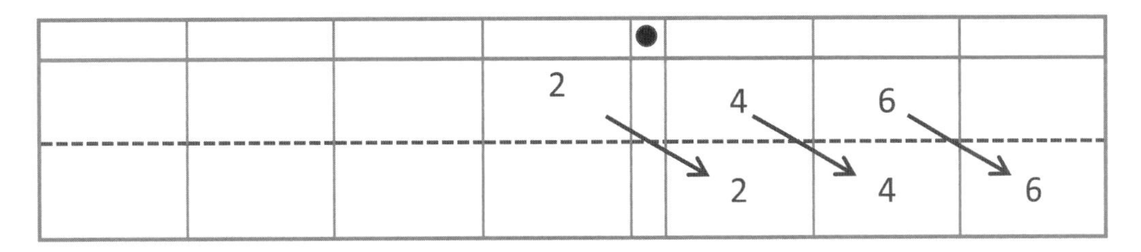

   b. $678 \div 100 =$ ____________

   c. $67 \div 1{,}000 =$ ____________

   d. Explain how and why the value of the 6 changed in the quotients in (a), (b), and (c).

3. Researchers counted 8,912 monarch butterflies on one branch of a tree at a site in Mexico. They estimated that the total number of butterflies at the site was 1,000 times as large. About how many butterflies were at the site in all? Explain your thinking, and include a statement of the solution.

4. A student used his place value chart to show a number. After the teacher instructed him to divide his number by 100, the chart showed 28.003. Draw a picture of what the place value chart looked like at first.

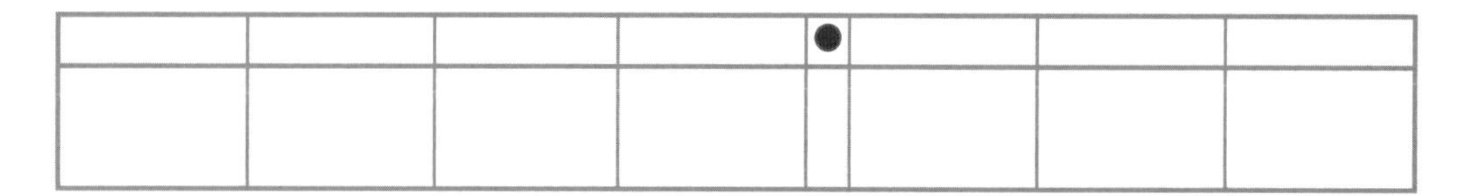

   a. Explain how you decided what to draw on your place value chart. Be sure to include your reasoning about how the value of each digit was affected by the division.

5. On a map, the perimeter of a park is 0.251 meters. The actual perimeter of the park is 1,000 times as large. What is the actual perimeter of the park? Explain how you know using a place value chart.

unlabeled hundreds through hundredths place value chart

1,000,000	100,000	10,000	1,000	100	10	1	.	$\frac{1}{10}$	$\frac{1}{100}$	$\frac{1}{1000}$
Millions	Hundred Thousands	Ten Thousands	Thousands	Hundreds	Tens	Ones	.	Tenths	Hundredths	Thousandths
							.			
							.			
							.			

millions through thousandths place value chart

Name ______________________________ Date ______________

1. Solve.

a. $54{,}000 \times 10 =$ ____________

b. $54{,}000 \div 10 =$ ____________

c. $8.7 \times 10 =$ ____________

d. $8.7 \div 10 =$ ____________

e. $0.13 \times 100 =$ ____________

f. $13 \div 1{,}000 =$ ____________

g. $3.12 \times 1{,}000 =$ ____________

h. $4{,}031.2 \div 100 =$ ____________

2. Find the products.

a. $19{,}340 \times 10 =$ ____________

b. $19{,}340 \times 100 =$ ____________

c. $19{,}340 \times 1{,}000 =$ ____________

d. Explain how you decided on the number of zeros in the products for (a), (b), and (c).

3. Find the quotients.

   a. 152 ÷ 10 = ____________________

   b. 152 ÷ 100 = ____________________

   c. 152 ÷ 1,000 = ____________________

   d. Explain how you decided where to place the decimal in the quotients for (a), (b), and (c).

4. Janice thinks that 20 hundredths is equivalent to 2 thousandths because 20 hundreds is equal to 2 thousands. Use words and a place value chart to correct Janice's error.

5. Canada has a population that is about $\frac{1}{10}$ as large as the United States. If Canada's population is about 32 million, about how many people live in the United States? Explain the number of zeros in your answer.

Name ______________________________ Date ______________

1. Solve.

a. 36,000 × 10 = ______________

b. 36,000 ÷ 10 = ______________

c. 4.3 × 10 = ______________

d. 4.3 ÷ 10 = ______________

e. 2.4 x 100 = ______________

f. 24 ÷ 1,000 = ______________

g. 4.54 × 1,000 = ______________

h. 3,045.4 ÷ 100 = ______________

2. Find the products.

a. 14,560 × 10 = ______________

b. 14,560 × 100 = ______________

c. 14,560 × 1,000 = ______________

Explain how you decided on the number of zeros in the products for (a), (b), and (c).

3. Find the quotients.

   a. $1.65 \div 10$ = ____________________

   b. $1.65 \div 100$ = ____________________

   c. Explain how you decided where to place the decimal in the quotients for (a) and (b).

4. Ted says that 3 tenths multiplied by 100 equals 300 thousandths. Is he correct? Use a place value chart to explain your answer.

5. Alaska has a land area of about 1,700,000 square kilometers. Florida has a land area $\frac{1}{10}$ the size of Alaska. What is the land area of Florida? Explain how you found your answer.

Name ______________________________ Date ________________

1. Write the following in exponential form (e.g., $100 = 10^2$).

a. 10,000 = __________

b. 1,000 = __________

c. 10×10 = __________

d. 100×100 = __________

e. 1,000,000 = __________

f. $1{,}000 \times 1{,}000$ = __________

2. Write the following in standard form (e.g., $5 \times 10^2 = 500$).

a. 9×10^3 = __________

b. 39×10^4 = __________

c. $7{,}200 \div 10^2$ = __________

d. $7{,}200{,}000 \div 10^3$ = __________

e. 4.025×10^3 = __________

f. 40.25×10^4 = __________

g. $72.5 \div 10^2$ = __________

h. $7.2 \div 10^2$ = __________

3. Think about the answers to Problem 2(a–d). Explain the pattern used to find an answer when you multiply or divide a whole number by a power of 10.

4. Think about the answers to Problem 2(e–h). Explain the pattern used to place the decimal in the answer when you multiply or divide a decimal by a power of 10.

5. Complete the patterns.

   a. 0.03 0.3 ______________ 30 ______________ ______________

   b. 6,500,000 65,000 ______________ 6.5 ______________

   c. ______________ 9,430 ______________ 94.3 9.43 ______________

   d. 999 9990 99,900 ______________ ______________ ______________

   e. ______________ 7.5 750 75,000 ______________ ______________

   f. Explain how you found the unknown numbers in set (b). Be sure to include your reasoning about the number of zeros in your numbers and how you placed the decimal.

   g. Explain how you found the unknown numbers in set (d). Be sure to include your reasoning about the number of zeros in your numbers and how you placed the decimal.

6. Shaunnie and Marlon missed the lesson on exponents. Shaunnie incorrectly wrote $10^5 = 50$ on her paper, and Marlon incorrectly wrote $2.5 \times 10^2 = 2.500$ on his paper.

   a. What mistake has Shaunnie made? Explain using words, numbers, or pictures why her thinking is incorrect and what she needs to do to correct her answer.

   b. What mistake has Marlon made? Explain using words, numbers, or pictures why his thinking is incorrect and what he needs to do to correct his answer.

Name ______________________________ Date ______________

1. Write the following in exponential form (e.g., $100 = 10^2$).

a. $1000 =$ __________

b. $10 \times 10 =$ __________

c. $100{,}000 =$ __________

d. $100 \times 10 =$ __________

e. $1{,}000{,}000 =$ __________

f. $10{,}000 \times 10 =$ __________

2. Write the following in standard form (e.g., $4 \times 10^2 = 400$).

a. $4 \times 10^3 =$ __________

b. $64 \times 10^4 =$ __________

c. $5{,}300 \div 10^2 =$ __________

d. $5{,}300{,}000 \div 10^3 =$ __________

e. $6.072 \times 10^3 =$ __________

f. $60.72 \times 10^4 =$ __________

g. $948 \div 10^3 =$ __________

h. $9.4 \div 10^2 =$ __________

3. Complete the patterns.

a. 0.02 0.2 __________ 20 __________ __________

b. 3,400,000 34,000 __________ 3.4 __________

c. __________ 8,570 __________ 85.7 8.57 __________

d. 444 4440 44,400 __________ __________ __________

e. __________ 9.5 950 95,000 __________ __________

4. After a lesson on exponents, Tia went home and said to her mom, "I learned that 10^4 is the same as 40,000." She has made a mistake in her thinking. Use words, numbers, or a place value chart to help Tia correct her mistake.

5. Solve $247 \div 10^2$ and 247×10^2.

   a. What is different about the two answers? Use words, numbers, or pictures to explain how the digits shift.

   b. Based on the answers from the pair of expressions above, solve $247 \div 10^3$ and 247×10^3.

10	10 × ___	

powers of 10 chart

Name ______________________________ Date ______________

1. Convert and write an equation with an exponent. Use your meter strip when it helps you.

   a. 3 meters to centimeters 3 m = 300 cm $3 \times 10^2 = 300$

   b. 105 centimeters to meters 105 cm = ______ m ______________

   c. 1.68 meters to centimeters ______ m = ______ cm ______________

   d. 80 centimeters to meters ______ cm = ______ m ______________

   e. 9.2 meters to centimeters ______ m = ______ cm ______________

   f. 4 centimeters to meters ______ cm = ______ m ______________

   g. In the space below, list the letters of the problems where larger units are converted to smaller units.

2. Convert using an equation with an exponent. Use your meter strip when it helps you.

   a. 3 meters to millimeters ______ m = ______ mm ______________

   b. 1.2 meters to millimeters ______ m = ______ mm ______________

   c. 1,020 millimeters to meters ______ mm = ______ m ______________

   d. 97 millimeters to meters ______ mm = ______ m ______________

   e. 7.28 meters to millimeters ______ m = ______ mm ______________

   f. 4 millimeters to meters ______ mm = ______ m ______________

   g. In the space below, list the letters of the problems where smaller units are converted to larger units.

3. Read each aloud as you write the equivalent measures. Write an equation with an exponent you might use to convert.

a. 3.512 m = ______________ mm $3.512 \times 10^3 = 3{,}512$

b. 8 cm = ______________ m ______________________

c. 42 mm = ______________ m ______________________

d. 0.05 m = ______________ mm ______________________

e. 0.002 m = ______________ cm ______________________

4. The length of the bar for a high jump competition must always be 4.75 m. Express this measurement in millimeters. Explain your thinking. Include an equation with an exponent in your explanation.

5. A honey bee's length measures 1 cm. Express this measurement in meters. Explain your thinking. Include an equation with an exponent in your explanation.

6. Explain why converting from meters to centimeters uses a different exponent than converting from meters to millimeters.

Name ______________________________ Date ______________

1. Convert and write an equation with an exponent. Use your meter strip when it helps you.

   a. 2 meters to centimeters 2m = 200 cm $2 \times 10^2 = 200$

   b. 108 centimeters to meters 108 cm = ______ m ______________

   c. 2.49 meters to centimeters ______ m = ______ cm ______________

   d. 50 centimeters to meters ______ cm = ______ m ______________

   e. 6.3 meters to centimeters ______ m = ______ cm ______________

   f. 7 centimeters to meters ______ cm = ______ m ______________

   g. In the space below, list the letters of the problems where smaller units are converted to larger units.

2. Convert using an equation with an exponent. Use your meter strip when it helps you.

   a. 4 meters to millimeters ______ m = ______ mm ______________

   b. 1.7 meters to millimeters ______ m = ______ mm ______________

   c. 1,050 millimeters to meters ______ mm = ______ m ______________

   d. 65 millimeters to meters ______ mm = ______ m ______________

   e. 4.92 meters to millimeters ______ m = ______ mm ______________

   f. 3 millimeters to meters ______ mm = ______ m ______________

   g. In the space below, list the letters of the problems where larger units are converted to smaller units.

3. Read each aloud as you write the equivalent measures. Write an equation with an exponent you might use to convert.

   a. 2.638 m = ____________ mm $2.638 \times 10^3 = 2{,}638$

   b. 7 cm = ____________ m ____________________

   c. 39 mm = ____________ m ____________________

   d. 0.08 m = ____________ mm ____________________

   e. 0.005 m = ____________ cm ____________________

4. Yi Ting's height is 1.49 m. Express this measurement in millimeters. Explain your thinking. Include an equation with an exponent in your explanation.

5. A ladybug's length measures 2 cm. Express this measurement in meters. Explain your thinking. Include an equation with an exponent in your explanation.

6. The length of a sticky note measures 77 millimeters. Express this length in meters. Explain your thinking. Include an equation with an exponent in your explanation.

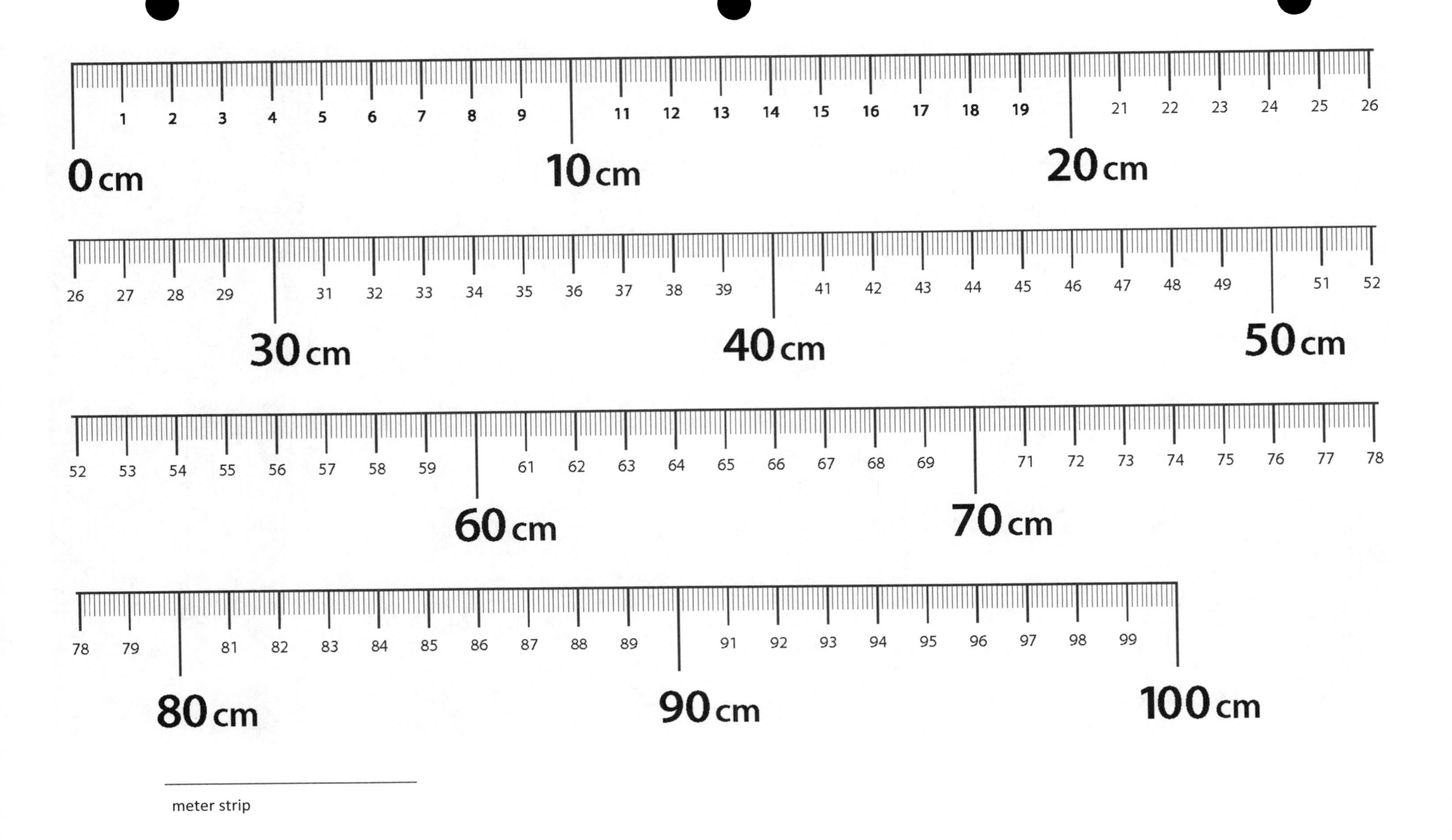

meter strip

Name ______________________________ Date ________________

1. Express as decimal numerals. The first one is done for you.

a. Four thousandths	0.004
b. Twenty-four thousandths	
c. One and three hundred twenty-four thousandths	
d. Six hundred eight thousandths	
e. Six hundred and eight thousandths	
f. $\frac{46}{1000}$	
g. $3\frac{946}{1000}$	
h. $200\frac{904}{1000}$	

2. Express each of the following values in words.

a. 0.005 ________________________________

b. 11.037 ________________________________

c. 403.608 ________________________________

3. Write the number on a place value chart. Then, write it in expanded form using fractions or decimals to express the decimal place value units. The first one is done for you.

a. 35.827

Tens	Ones		Tenths	Hundredths	Thousandths
3	5	•	8	2	7

$35.827 = 3 \times 10 + 5 \times 1 + 8 \times \left(\frac{1}{10}\right) + 2 \times \left(\frac{1}{100}\right) + 7 \times \left(\frac{1}{1000}\right)$ *or*

$= 3 \times 10 + 5 \times 1 + 8 \times 0.1 + 2 \times 0.01 + 7 \times 0.001$

b. 0.249

c. 57.281

4. Write a decimal for each of the following. Use a place value chart to help, if necessary.

a. $7 \times 10 + 4 \times 1 + 6 \times \left(\frac{1}{10}\right) + 9 \times \left(\frac{1}{100}\right) + 2 \times \left(\frac{1}{1000}\right)$

b. $5 \times 100 + 3 \times 10 + 8 \times 0.1 + 9 \times 0.001$

c. $4 \times 1{,}000 + 2 \times 100 + 7 \times 1 + 3 \times \left(\frac{1}{100}\right) + 4 \times \left(\frac{1}{1000}\right)$

5. Mr. Pham wrote 2.619 on the board. Christy says it is two and six hundred nineteen thousandths. Amy says it is 2 ones 6 tenths 1 hundredth 9 thousandths. Who is right? Use words and numbers to explain your answer.

Name ______________________________ Date ______________

1. Express as decimal numerals. The first one is done for you.

a. Five thousandths	0.005
b. Thirty-five thousandths	
c. Nine and two hundred thirty-five thousandths	
d. Eight hundred and five thousandths	
e. $\frac{8}{1000}$	
f. $\frac{28}{1000}$	
g. $7\frac{528}{1000}$	
h. $300\frac{502}{1000}$	

2. Express each of the following values in words.

a. 0.008 ______________________________

b. 15.062 ______________________________

c. 607.409 ______________________________

3. Write the number on a place value chart. Then, write it in expanded form using fractions or decimals to express the decimal place value units. The first one is done for you.

a. 27.346

Tens	Ones	•	Tenths	Hundredths	Thousandths
2	7		3	4	6

$27.346 = 2 \times 10 + 7 \times 1 + 3 \times \left(\frac{1}{10}\right) + 4 \times \left(\frac{1}{100}\right) + 6 \times \left(\frac{1}{1000}\right)$ *or*

$27.346 = 2 \times 10 + 7 \times 1 + 3 \times 0.1 + 4 \times 0.01 + 6 \times 0.001$

b. 0.362

c. 49.564

4. Write a decimal for each of the following. Use a place value chart to help, if necessary.

   a. $3 \times 10 + 5 \times 1 + 2 \times \left(\frac{1}{10}\right) + 7 \times \left(\frac{1}{100}\right) + 6 \times \left(\frac{1}{1000}\right)$

   b. $9 \times 100 + 2 \times 10 + 3 \times 0.1 + 7 \times 0.001$

   c. $5 \times 1000 + 4 \times 100 + 8 \times 1 + 6 \times \left(\frac{1}{100}\right) + 5 \times \left(\frac{1}{1000}\right)$

5. At the beginning of a lesson, a piece of chalk is 4.875 inches long. At the end of the lesson, it is 3.125 inches long. Write the two amounts in expanded form using fractions.

   a. At the beginning of the lesson:

   b. At the end of the lesson:

6. Mrs. Herman asked the class to write an expanded form for 412.638. Nancy wrote the expanded form using fractions, and Charles wrote the expanded form using decimals. Write their responses.

Thousands	Hundreds	Tens	Ones	Tenths	Hundredths	Thousandths

thousands through thousandths place value chart

Name ______________________________ Date ________________

1. Show the numbers on the place value chart using digits. Use >, <, or = to compare. Explain your thinking in the space to the right.

34.223 ◯ 34.232

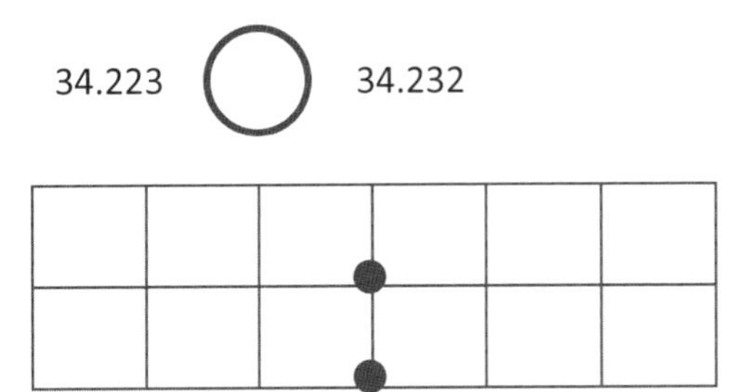

0.8 ◯ 0.706

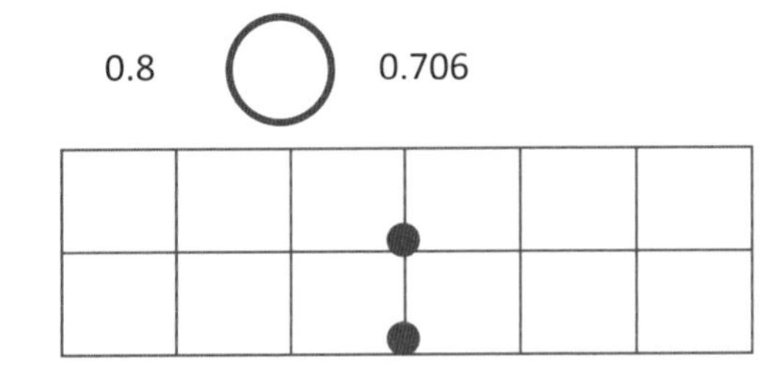

2. Use >, <, or = to compare the following. Use a place value chart to help, if necessary.

a. 16.3	◯	16.4
b. 0.83	◯	$\frac{83}{100}$
c. $\frac{205}{1000}$	◯	0.205
d. 95.580	◯	95.58
e. 9.1	◯	9.099
f. 8.3	◯	83 tenths
g. 5.8	◯	Fifty-eight hundredths
h. Thirty-six and nine thousandths	◯	4 tens

i. 202 hundredths	◯	2 hundreds and 2 thousandths
j. One hundred fifty-eight thousandths	◯	158,000
k. 4.15	◯	415 tenths

3. Arrange the numbers in increasing order.

   a. 3.049 3.059 3.05 3.04

   ____

   b. 182.205 182.05 182.105 182.025

   ____

4. Arrange the numbers in decreasing order.

   a. 7.608 7.68 7.6 7.068

   ____

   b. 439.216 439.126 439.612 439.261

   ____

5. Lance measured 0.485 liter of water. Angel measured 0.5 liter of water. Lance said, "My beaker has more water than yours because my number has three decimal places and yours only has one." Is Lance correct? Use words and numbers to explain your answer.

6. Dr. Hong prescribed 0.019 liter more medicine than Dr. Tannenbaum. Dr. Evans prescribed 0.02 less than Dr. Hong. Who prescribed the most medicine? Who prescribed the least?

Name ______________________________ Date ______________

1. Use >, <, or = to compare the following.

a. 16.45	◯	16.454
b. 0.83	◯	$\frac{83}{100}$
c. $\frac{205}{1000}$	◯	0.205
d. 95.045	◯	95.545
e. 419.10	◯	419.099
f. Five ones and eight tenths	◯	Fifty-eight tenths
g. Thirty-six and nine thousandths	◯	Four tens
h. One hundred four and twelve hundredths	◯	One hundred four and two thousandths
i. One hundred fifty-eight thousandths	◯	0.58
j. 703.005	◯	Seven hundred three and five hundredths

2. Arrange the numbers in increasing order.

a. 8.08 8.081 8.09 8.008

____

b. 14.204 14.200 14.240 14.210

____

3. Arrange the numbers in decreasing order.

   a. 8.508 8.58 7.5 7.058

   ____

   b. 439.216 439.126 439.612 439.261

   ____

4. James measured his hand. It was 0.17 meter. Jennifer measured her hand. It was 0.165 meter. Whose hand is bigger? How do you know?

5. In a paper airplane contest, Marcel's plane travels 3.345 meters. Salvador's plane travels 3.35 meters. Jennifer's plane travels 3.3 meters. Based on the measurements, whose plane traveled the farthest distance? Whose plane traveled the shortest distance? Explain your reasoning using a place value chart.

Name ______________________________ Date ________________

Fill in the table, and then round to the given place. Label the number lines to show your work. Circle the rounded number.

1. 3.1

a. Hundredths b. Tenths c. Tens

Tens	Ones	Tenths	Hundredths	Thousandths

2. 115.376

a. Hundredths b. Ones c. Tens

Tens	Ones	Tenths	Hundredths	Thousandths

3. 0.994

Tens	Ones	Tenths	Hundredths	Thousandths

a. Hundredths

b. Tenths

c. Ones

d. Tens

4. For open international competition, the throwing circle in the men's shot put must have a diameter of 2.135 meters. Round this number to the nearest hundredth. Use a number line to show your work.

5. Jen's pedometer said she walked 2.549 miles. She rounded her distance to 3 miles. Her brother rounded her distance to 2.5 miles. When they argued about it, their mom said they were both right. Explain how that could be true. Use number lines and words to explain your reasoning.

Name ______________________________ Date ______________

Fill in the table, and then round to the given place. Label the number lines to show your work. Circle the rounded number.

1. 4.3

a. Hundredths b. Tenths c. Ones

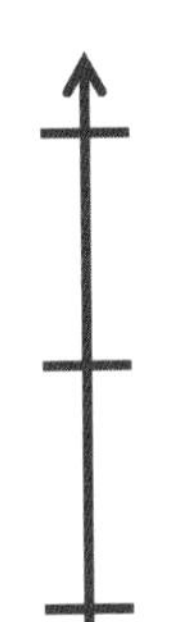

Tens	Ones	Tenths	Hundredths	Thousandths

2. 225.286

a. Hundredths b. Ones c. Tens

Tens	Ones	Tenths	Hundredths	Thousandths

3. 8.984

Tens	Ones	Tenths	Hundredths	Thousandths

a. Hundredths b. Tenths c. Ones d. Tens

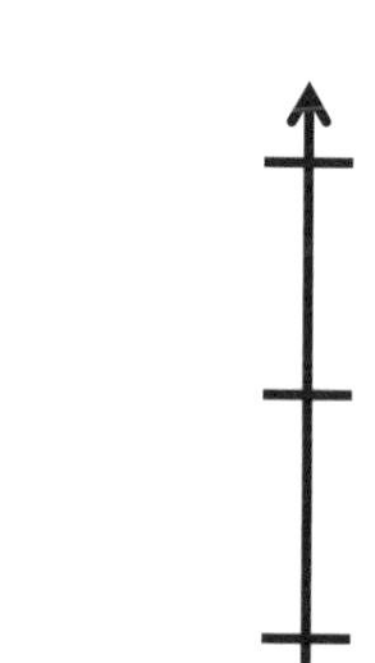

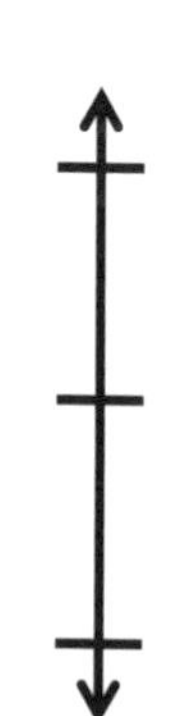

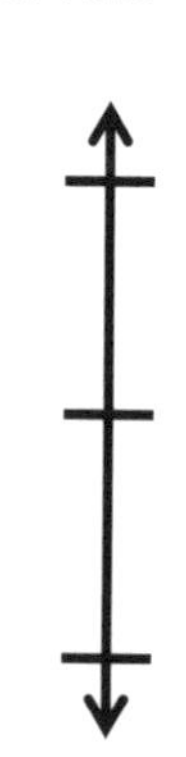

4. On a Major League Baseball diamond, the distance from the pitcher's mound to home plate is 18.386 meters.

   a. Round this number to the nearest hundredth of a meter. Use a number line to show your work.

   b. How many centimeters is it from the pitcher's mound to home plate?

5. Jules reads that 1 pint is equivalent to 0.473 liters. He asks his teacher how many liters there are in a pint. His teacher responds that there are about 0.47 liters in a pint. He asks his parents, and they say there are about 0.5 liters in a pint. Jules says they are both correct. How can that be true? Explain your answer.

Hundreds	Tens	Ones	•	Tenths	Hundredths	Thousandths

hundreds to thousandths place value chart

Name ______________________________ Date ______________

1. Write the decomposition that helps you, and then round to the given place value. Draw number lines to explain your thinking. Circle the rounded value on each number line.

   a. Round 32.697 to the nearest tenth, hundredth, and one.

   b. Round 141.999 to the nearest tenth, hundredth, ten, and hundred.

2. A root beer factory produces 132,554 cases in 100 days. About how many cases does the factory produce in 1 day? Round your answer to the nearest tenth of a case. Show your thinking on the number line.

3. A decimal number has two digits to the right of its decimal point. If we round it to the nearest tenth, the result is 13.7.

   a. What is the maximum possible value of this number? Use words and the number line to explain your reasoning. Include the midpoint on your number line.

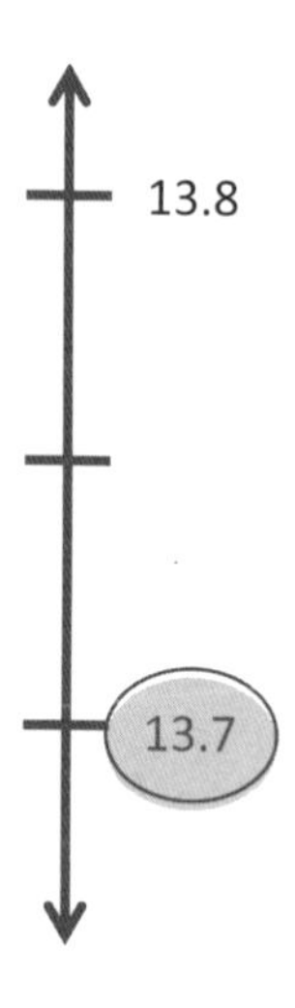

   b. What is the minimum possible value of this decimal? Use words and the number line to explain your reasoning. Include the midpoint on your number line.

Name ______________________________ Date ________________

1. Write the decomposition that helps you, and then round to the given place value. Draw number lines to explain your thinking. Circle the rounded value on each number line.

   a. 43.586 to the nearest tenth, hundredth, and one.

   b. 243.875 to nearest tenth, hundredth, ten, and hundred.

2. A trip from New York City to Seattle is 2,852.1 miles. A family wants to make the drive in 10 days, driving the same number of miles each day. About how many miles will they drive each day? Round your answer to the nearest tenth of a mile.

3. A decimal number has two digits to the right of its decimal point. If we round it to the nearest tenth, the result is 18.6.

   a. What is the maximum possible value of this number? Use words and the number line to explain your reasoning. Include the midpoint on your number line.

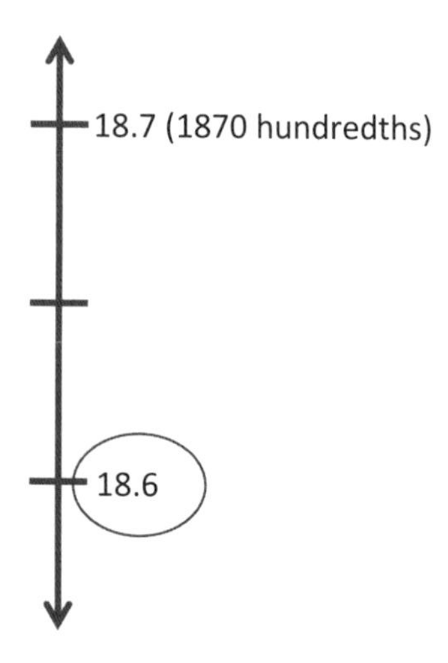

   b. What is the minimum possible value of this decimal? Use words, pictures, or numbers to explain your reasoning.

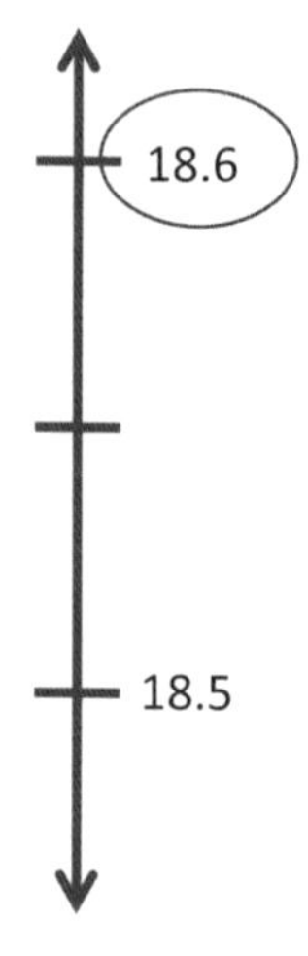

Name ______________________________ Date ______________

1. Solve, and then write the sum in standard form. Use a place value chart if necessary.

   a. 1 tenth + 2 tenths = __________ tenths = __________

   b. 14 tenths + 9 tenths = __________ tenths = ________ one(s) _______ tenth(s) = __________

   c. 1 hundredth + 2 hundredths = __________ hundredths = __________

   d. 27 hundredths + 5 hundredths = _____ hundredths = ______ tenths ______ hundredths = ______

   e. 1 thousandth + 2 thousandths = ________ thousandths = __________

   f. 35 thousandths + 8 thousandths = ____ thousandths = ____ hundredths ____ thousandths = ______

   g. 6 tenths + 3 thousandths = __________ thousandths = ________

   h. 7 ones 2 tenths + 4 tenths = __________ tenths = ________

   i. 2 thousandths + 9 ones 5 thousandths = __________ thousandths = __________

2. Solve using the standard algorithm.

a. 0.3+ 0.82 = __________	b. 1.03 + 0.08 = __________
c. 7.3 + 2.8 = __________	d. 57.03 + 2.08 = __________

e. 62.573 + 4.328 = ___________	f. 85.703 + 12.197 = ___________

3. Van Cortlandt Park's walking trail is 1.02 km longer than Marine Park. Central Park's walking trail is 0.242 km longer than Van Cortlandt's.

   a. Fill in the missing information in the chart below.

New York City Walking Trails	
Central Park	________ km
Marine Park	1.28 km
Van Cortlandt Park	________ km

   b. If a tourist walked all 3 trails in a day, how many kilometers would he or she have walked?

4. Meyer has 0.64 GB of space remaining on his iPod. He wants to download a pedometer app (0.24 GB), a photo app (0.403 GB), and a math app (0.3 GB). Which combinations of apps can he download? Explain your thinking.

Name ______________________________ Date ______________

1. Solve.

   a. 3 tenths + 4 tenths = __________ tenths

   b. 12 tenths + 9 tenths = __________ tenths = __________ one(s) __________ tenth(s)

   c. 3 hundredths + 4 hundredths = __________ hundredths

   d. 27 hundredths + 7 hundredths = ______ hundredths = ______ tenths ______ hundredths

   e. 4 thousandths + 3 thousandths = __________ thousandths

   f. 39 thousandths + 5 thousandths = ____ thousandths = ____ hundredths ____ thousandths

   g. 5 tenths + 7 thousandths = __________ thousandths

   h. 4 ones 4 tenths + 4 tenths = __________ tenths

   i. 8 thousandths + 6 ones 8 thousandths = __________ thousandths

2. Solve using the standard algorithm.

a. 0.4 + 0.7 = __________	b. 2.04 + 0.07 = __________
c. 6.4 + 3.7 = __________	d. 56.04 + 3.07 = __________

e. 72.564 + 5.137 = ____________	f. 75.604 + 22.296 = ____________

3. Walkway Over the Hudson, a bridge that crosses the Hudson River in Poughkeepsie, is 2.063 kilometers long. Anping Bridge, which was built in China 850 years ago, is 2.07 kilometers long.

   a. What is the total span of both bridges? Show your thinking.

   b. Leah likes to walk her dog on the Walkway Over the Hudson. If she walks across and back, how far will she and her dog walk?

4. For his parents' anniversary, Danny spends $5.87 on a photo. He also buys a balloon for $2.49 and a box of strawberries for $4.50. How much money does he spend all together?

Name ______________________________ Date ______________

1. Subtract, writing the difference in standard form. You may use a place value chart to solve.

   a. 5 tenths – 2 tenths = _______tenths = _______

   b. 5 ones 9 thousandths – 2 ones = _______ones _______thousandths = _______

   c. 7 hundreds 8 hundredths – 4 hundredths = _______ hundreds _______ hundredths = _______

   d. 37 thousandths – 16 thousandths = _______thousandths = _______

2. Solve using the standard algorithm.

a. 1.4 – 0.7 = _______	b. 91.49 – 0.7 = _______	c. 191.49 – 10.72 = _______
d. 7.148 – 0.07 = _______	e. 60.91 – 2.856 = _______	f. 361.31 – 2.841 = _______

3. Solve.

a. 10 tens – 1 ten 1 tenth	b. 3 – 22 tenths	c. 37 tenths – 1 one 2 tenths
d. 8 ones 9 hundredths – 3.4	e. 5.622 – 3 hundredths	f. 2 ones 4 tenths – 0.59

4. Mrs. Fan wrote *5 tenths minus 3 hundredths* on the board. Michael said the answer is 2 tenths because 5 minus 3 is 2. Is he correct? Explain.

5. A pen costs $2.09. It costs $0.45 less than a marker. Ken paid for one pen and one marker with a five dollar bill. Use a tape diagram with calculations to determine his change.

Name ______________________________ Date ______________

1. Subtract. You may use a place value chart.

   a. 9 tenths – 3 tenths = __________tenths

   b. 9 ones 2 thousandths – 3 ones = __________ones __________thousandths

   c. 4 hundreds 6 hundredths – 3 hundredths = __________hundreds __________hundredths

   d. 56 thousandths – 23 thousandths = ________thousandths = ________hundredths ______thousandths

2. Solve using the standard algorithm.

a. 1.8 – 0.9 = __________	b. 41.84 – 0.9 = __________	c. 341.84 – 21.92 = __________
d. 5.182 – 0.09 = __________	e. 50.416 – 4.25 = __________	f. 741 – 3.91 = __________

3. Solve.

a. 30 tens – 3 tens 3 tenths	b. 5 – 16 tenths	c. 24 tenths – 1 one 3 tenths
d. 6 ones 7 hundredths – 2.3	e. 8.246 – 5 hundredths	f. 5 ones 3 tenths – 0.53

4. Mr. House wrote *8 tenths minus 5 hundredths* on the board. Maggie said the answer is 3 hundredths because 8 minus 5 is 3. Is she correct? Explain.

5. A clipboard costs $2.23. It costs $0.58 more than a notebook. Lisa bought two clipboards and one notebook. She paid with a ten dollar bill. How much change does Lisa get? Use a tape diagram to show your thinking.

Name ______________________________ Date ______________

1. Solve by drawing disks on a place value chart. Write an equation, and express the product in standard form.

a. 3 copies of 2 tenths

b. 5 groups of 2 hundredths

c. 3 times 6 tenths

d. 6 times 4 hundredths

e. 5 times as much as 7 tenths

f. 4 thousandths times 3

2. Draw a model similar to the one pictured below for Parts (b), (c), and (d). Find the sum of the partial products to evaluate each expression.

a. 7×3.12

	3 ones +	1 tenth +	2 hundredths
7	7×3 ones	7×1 tenth	7×2 hundredths

______ + ______ + 0.14 = ______

b. 6×4.25

c. 3 copies of 4.65

d. 4 times as much as 20.075

3. Miles incorrectly gave the product of 7×2.6 as 14.42. Use a place value chart or an area model to help Miles understand his mistake.

4. Mrs. Zamir wants to buy 8 protractors and some erasers for her classroom. She has $30. If protractors cost $2.65 each, how much will Mrs. Zamir have left to buy erasers?

Name ____________________________________ Date ____________________

1. Solve by drawing disks on a place value chart. Write an equation, and express the product in standard form.

   a. 2 copies of 4 tenths

   b. 4 groups of 5 hundredths

   c. 4 times 7 tenths

   d. 3 times 5 hundredths

   e. 9 times as much as 7 tenths

   f. 6 thousandths times 8

2. Draw a model similar to the one pictured below. Find the sum of the partial products to evaluate each expression.

   a. 4×6.79

	6 ones +	7 tenths +	9 hundredths
4	4×6 ones	4×7 tenths	4×9 hundredths

______ + ______ + ______ = ______

b. 6×7.49

c. 9 copies of 3.65

d. 3 times 20.175

3. Leanne multiplied 8×4.3 and got 32.24. Is Leanne correct? Use an area model to explain your answer.

4. Anna buys groceries for her family. Hamburger meat is \$3.38 per pound, sweet potatoes are \$0.79 each, and hamburger rolls are \$2.30 a bag. If Anna buys 3 pounds of meat, 5 sweet potatoes, and 1 bag of hamburger rolls, what will she pay in all for the groceries?

Name ______________________________ Date ________________

1. Choose the reasonable product for each expression. Explain your reasoning in the spaces below using words, pictures, or numbers.

a. 2.5×4	0.1	1	10	100
b. 3.14×7	2198	219.8	21.98	2.198
c. 8×6.022	4.8176	48.176	481.76	4817.6
d. 9×5.48	493.2	49.32	4.932	0.4932

2. Pedro is building a spice rack with 4 shelves that are each 0.55 meter long. At the hardware store, Pedro finds that he can only buy the shelving in whole meter lengths. Exactly how many meters of shelving does Pedro need? Since he can only buy whole number lengths, how many meters of shelving should he buy? Justify your thinking.

3. Marcel rides his bicycle to school and back on Tuesdays and Thursdays. He lives 3.62 kilometers away from school. Marcel's gym teacher wants to know about how many kilometers he bikes in a week. Marcel's math teacher wants to know exactly how many kilometers he bikes in a week. What should Marcel tell each teacher? Show your work.

4. The poetry club had its first bake sale, and they made \$79.35. The club members are planning to have 4 more bake sales. Leslie said, "If we make the same amount at each bake sale, we'll earn \$3,967.50." Peggy said, "No way, Leslie! We'll earn \$396.75 after five bake sales." Use estimation to help Peggy explain why Leslie's reasoning is inaccurate. Show your reasoning using words, numbers, or pictures.

Name ______________________________ Date ______________

1. Choose the reasonable product for each expression. Explain your thinking in the spaces below using words, pictures, or numbers.

a. 2.1×3 0.63 6.3 63 630

b. 4.27×6 2562 256.2 25.62 2.562

c. 7×6.053 4237.1 423.71 42.371 4.2371

d. 9×4.82 4.338 43.38 433.8 4338

2. Yi Ting weighs 8.3 kg. Her older brother is 4 times as heavy as Yi Ting. How much does her older brother weigh in kilograms?

3. Tim is painting his storage shed. He buys 4 gallons of white paint, and 3 gallons of blue paint. Each gallon of white paint costs $15.72, and each gallon of blue paints is $21.87. How much will Tim spend in all on paint?

4. Ribbon is sold at 3 yards for $6.33. Jackie bought 24 yards of ribbon for a project. How much did she pay?

Name ______________________________ Date ______________

1. Complete the sentences with the correct number of units, and then complete the equation.

   a. 4 groups of ______ tenths is 1.6. $1.6 \div 4 =$ __________

   b. 8 groups of ______ hundredths is 0.32. $0.32 \div 8 =$ __________

   c. 7 groups of ______ thousandths is 0.084. $0.084 \div 7 =$ __________

   d. 5 groups of ______ tenths is 2.0. $2.0 \div 5 =$ __________

2. Complete the number sentence. Express the quotient in units and then in standard form.

   a. $4.2 \div 7 =$ __________ tenths $\div 7 =$ __________ tenths = __________

   b. $2.64 \div 2 =$ __________ ones $\div 2$ + __________ hundredths $\div 2$

   = __________ ones + __________ hundredths

   = __________

   c. $12.64 \div 2 =$ __________ ones $\div 2$ + __________ hundredths $\div 2$

   = __________ ones + __________ hundredths

   = __________

d. 4.26 ÷ 6 = ____________ tenths ÷ 6 + ____________ hundredths ÷ 6

= ______________________________________

= ______________________________________

e. 4.236 ÷ 6 = ______________________________________

= ______________________________________

= ______________________________________

3. Find the quotients. Then, use words, numbers, or pictures to describe any relationships you notice between each pair of problems and quotients.

a. 32 ÷ 8 = ______________ 3.2 ÷ 8 = ______________

b. 81 ÷ 9 = ______________ 0.081 ÷ 9 = ______________

4. Are the quotients below reasonable? Explain your answers.

a. 5.6 ÷ 7 = 8

b. 56 ÷ 7 = 0.8

c. .56 ÷ 7 = 0.08

5. 12.48 milliliters of medicine were separated into doses of 4 mL each. How many doses were made?

6. The price of milk in 2013 was around $3.28 a gallon. This was eight times as much as you would have probably paid for a gallon of milk in the 1950s. What was the cost for a gallon of milk during the 1950s? Use a tape diagram, and show your calculations.

Name ______________________________ Date ______________

1. Complete the sentences with the correct number of units, and then complete the equation.

   a. 3 groups of ______ tenths is 1.5. $1.5 \div 3 =$ ____________

   b. 6 groups of ______ hundredths is 0.24. $0.24 \div 6 =$ ____________

   c. 5 groups of ______ thousandths is 0.045. $0.045 \div 5 =$ ____________

2. Complete the number sentence. Express the quotient in units and then in standard form.

   a. $9.36 \div 3 =$ __________ ones $\div 3$ + __________ hundredths $\div 3$

      = __________ ones + __________ hundredths

      = __________

   b. $36.012 \div 3 =$ __________ ones $\div 3$ + __________ thousandths $\div 3$

      = __________ ones + __________ thousandths

      = __________

   c. $3.55 \div 5 =$ __________ tenths $\div 5$ + __________ hundredths $\div 5$

      = ______________________________

      = ______________________________

d. 3.545 ÷ 5 = ____________________

= ____________________

= ____________________

3. Find the quotients. Then, use words, numbers, or pictures to describe any relationships you notice between each pair of problems and quotients.

a. 21 ÷ 7 = ____________ 2.1 ÷ 7 = ____________

b. 48 ÷ 8 = ____________ 0.048 ÷ 8 = ____________

4. Are the quotients below reasonable? Explain your answers.

a. 0.54 ÷ 6 = 9

b. 5.4 ÷ 6 = 0.9

c. $54 \div 6 = 0.09$

5. A toy airplane costs $4.84. It costs 4 times as much as a toy car. What is the cost of the toy car?

6. Julian bought 3.9 liters of cranberry juice, and Jay bought 8.74 liters of apple juice. They mixed the two juices together, and then poured them equally into 2 bottles. How many liters of juice are in each bottle?

Name ______________________________ Date ________________

1. Draw place value disks on the place value chart to solve. Show each step using the standard algorithm.

   a. 4.236 ÷ 3 = ______

Ones	Tenths	Hundredths	Thousandths

3 ⟌ 4 . 2 3 6

   b. 1.324 ÷ 2 = ______

Ones	Tenths	Hundredths	Thousandths

2 ⟌ 1 . 3 2 4

2. Solve using the standard algorithm.

a. $0.78 \div 3 =$ ______	b. $7.28 \div 4 =$ ______	c. $17.45 \div 5 =$ ______

3. Grayson wrote $1.47 \div 7 = 2.1$ in her math journal.
Use words, numbers, or pictures to explain why Grayson's thinking is incorrect.

4. Mrs. Nguyen used 1.48 meters of netting to make 4 identical mini hockey goals. How much netting did she use per goal?

5. Esperanza usually buys avocados for $0.94 apiece. During a sale, she gets 5 avocados for $4.10. How much money did she save per avocado? Use a tape diagram and show your calculations.

Name ______________________________ Date ____________

1. Draw place value disks on the place value chart to solve. Show each step using the standard algorithm.

a. 5.241 ÷ 3 = ______

Ones	Tenths	Hundredths	Thousandths

$3\overline{)5.241}$

b. 5.372 ÷ 4 = ______

Ones	Tenths	Hundredths	Thousandths

$4\overline{)5.372}$

2. Solve using the standard algorithm.

a. 0.64 ÷ 4 = ______	b. 6.45 ÷ 5 = ______	c. 16.404 ÷ 6 = ______

3. Mrs. Mayuko paid $40.68 for 3 kg of shrimp. What's the cost of 1 kilogram of shrimp?

4. The total weight of 6 pieces of butter and a bag of sugar is 3.8 lb. If the weight of the bag of sugar is 1.4 lb, what is the weight of each piece of butter?

Name ______________________________ Date ____________________

1. Draw place value disks on the place value chart to solve. Show each step in the standard algorithm.

a. 0.5 ÷ 2 = _______

Ones	●	Tenths	Hundredths	Thousandths

$$2\overline{)0.5}$$

b. 5.7 ÷ 4 = _______

Ones	●	Tenths	Hundredths	Thousandths

$$4\overline{)5.7}$$

2. Solve using the standard algorithm.

a. $0.9 \div 2 =$	b. $9.1 \div 5 =$	c. $9 \div 6 =$
d. $0.98 \div 4 =$	e. $9.3 \div 6 =$	f. $91 \div 4 =$

3. Six bakers shared 7.5 kilograms of flour equally. How much flour did they each receive?

4. Mrs. Henderson makes punch by mixing 10.9 liters of apple juice, 0.6 liters of orange juice, and 8 liters of ginger ale. She pours the mixture equally into 6 large punch bowls. How much punch is in each bowl? Express your answer in liters.

Name _______________________________ Date ______________

1. Draw place value disks on the place value chart to solve. Show each step in the standard algorithm.

a. 0.7 ÷ 4 = ______

Ones	•	Tenths	Hundredths	Thousandths

$4 \overline{)\,0.7}$

b. 8.1 ÷ 5 = ______

Ones	•	Tenths	Hundredths	Thousandths

$5 \overline{)\,8.1}$

2. Solve using the standard algorithm.

a. $0.7 \div 2 =$	b. $3.9 \div 6 =$	c. $9 \div 4 =$
d. $0.92 \div 2 =$	e. $9.4 \div 4 =$	f. $91 \div 8 =$

3. A rope 8.7 meters long is cut into 5 equal pieces. How long is each piece?

4. Yasmine bought 6 gallons of apple juice. After filling up 4 bottles of the same size with apple juice, she had 0.3 gallon of apple juice left. How many gallons of apple juice are in each container?

Name ______________________________ Date ________________

Solve.

1. Mr. Frye distributed \$126 equally among his 4 children for their weekly allowance.
   a. How much money did each child receive?

   b. John, the oldest child, paid his siblings to do his chores. If John pays his allowance equally to his brother and two sisters, how much money will each of his siblings have received in all?

2. Ava is 23 cm taller than Olivia, and Olivia is half the height of Lucas. If Lucas is 1.78 m tall, how tall are Ava and Olivia? Express their heights in centimeters.

3. Mr. Hower can buy a computer with a down payment of $510 and 8 monthly payments of $35.75. If he pays cash for the computer, the cost is $699.99. How much money will he save if he pays cash for the computer instead of paying for it in monthly payments?

4. Brandon mixed 6.83 lb of cashews with 3.57 lb of pistachios. After filling up 6 bags that were the same size with the mixture, he had 0.35 lb of nuts left. What was the weight of each bag? Use a tape diagram and show your calculations.

5. The bakery bought 4 bags of flour containing 3.5 kg each. 0.475 kg of flour is needed to make a batch of muffins, and 0.65 kg is needed to make a loaf of bread.

   a. If 4 batches of muffins and 5 loaves of bread are baked, how much flour will be left? Give your answer in kilograms.

   b. The remaining flour is stored in bins that hold 3 kg each. How many bins will be needed to store the flour? Explain your answer.

Name ______________________________ Date ________________

Solve using tape diagrams.

1. A gardener installed 42.6 meters of fencing in a week. He installed 13.45 meters on Monday and 9.5 meters on Tuesday. He installed the rest of the fence in equal lengths on Wednesday through Friday. How many meters of fencing did he install on each of the last three days?

2. Jenny charges $9.15 an hour to babysit toddlers and $7.45 an hour to babysit school-aged children.

   a. If Jenny babysat toddlers for 9 hours and school-aged children for 6 hours, how much money did she earn in all?

   b. Jenny wants to earn $1,300 by the end of the summer. How much more will she need to earn to meet her goal?

3. A table and 8 chairs weigh 235.68 lb together. If the table weighs 157.84 lb, what is the weight of one chair in pounds?

4. Mrs. Cleaver mixes 1.24 liters of red paint with 3 times as much blue paint to make purple paint. She pours the paint equally into 5 containers. How much blue paint is in each container? Give your answer in liters.